**DK** READERS

PROFICIENT
**4**
READERS

# CURSE of the CROCODILE GOD

Written by Stewart Ross
Illustrated by Inklink

## CURSE OF THE CROCODILE GOD

Methen's story takes place 4,000 years ago in Ancient Egypt. It is the year 1795 BCE, and the ruler of Egypt is Pharaoh Sobekneferu. Our hero and his new friend Madja live in a town near Hawara in northern Egypt. Turn to page 42 to see a map of Ancient Egypt and a timeline, then let the story begin....

"MY NAME IS METHEN, and this is my friend Madja. Our lives are in great danger! We are caught in a fiendish plot hatched by a corrupt official. As the son of a respected priest, nothing in my life has prepared me for this. My days have been spent at scribe school, learning to read and write. Madja is a serving girl in a nobleman's court. Like me, she is 13 years old, but our paths had never crossed until the evening of the banquet at Lord Ini's palace."

# A Note to P[arents]

DK READERS is a compelling programme for beginning readers, designed in conjunction with literacy experts, including Maureen Fernandes, B.Ed (Hons). Maureen has spent many years teaching literacy, both in the classroom and as a consultant in schools.

Beautiful illustrations and superb full-colour photographs combine with engaging, easy-to-read stories to offer a fresh approach to each subject in the series.

Each DK READER is guaranteed to capture a child's interest while developing his or her reading skills, general knowledge and love of reading.

The five levels of DK READERS are aimed at different reading abilities, enabling you to choose the books that are exactly right for your child:

**Pre-level 1:** Learning to read
**Level 1:** Beginning to read
**Level 2:** Beginning to read alone
**Level 3:** Reading alone
**Level 4:** Proficient readers

The "normal" age at which a child begins to read can be anywhere from three to eight years old. Adult participation through the lower levels is very helpful for providing encouragement, discussing storylines and sounding out unfamiliar words.

No matter which level you select, you can be sure that you are helping your child learn to read, then read to learn!

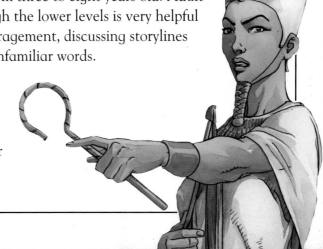

**DK**

LONDON, NEW YORK, MUNICH,
MELBOURNE, AND DELHI

**Editor** Kate Simkins
**Designers** Cathy Tincknell
and John Kelly
**Senior Editor** Catherine Saunders
**Brand Manager** Lisa Lanzarini
**Publishing Manager** Simon Beecroft
**Category Publisher** Alex Allan
**DTP Designer** Hanna Ländin
**Production** Rochelle Talary

**Reading Consultant**
Maureen Fernandes

Published in Great Britain in 2007 by
Dorling Kindersley Limited,
80 Strand, London WC2R 0RL

Some material contained in this book was previously published in
2003 in *Tales of the Dead: Ancient Egypt.*

07 08 09 10 10 9 8 7 6 5 4 3 2 1

Copyright © 2007 Dorling Kindersley Limited

A CIP record for this book is available from the British Library.

ISBN: 978-1-40531-838-9

High-res workflow proofed by Media Development
and Printing Ltd, UK.
Design and digital artworking by John Kelly and Cathy Tincknell.
Printed and bound in China by L. Rex Printing Co. Ltd.

All artwork by Inklink except the illustrations of the town, the
temple and the pharaoh on page 42, the servant, marriage contract,
prisoners, Chief Embalmer and Lord Ini's Palace on page 43, the
pyramid, burial chamber, and the robbers on page 44, the soldiers
and the House of the Dead on page 45, the priest and the temple on
page 46, and the natron table on page 48 by Richard Bonson.

Discover more at
**www.dk.com**

# Contents

THE SILVER MOON LIT OUR WAY ACROSS THE DESERT AS MY FATHER LED ME INTO **TOWN**.

I NEVER EVEN WANTED TO GO.

FATHER MADE ME.

IT IS THE WISH OF LORD INI TO MEET YOU, METHEN.

*Words in **bold** appear in the glossary on page 42.*

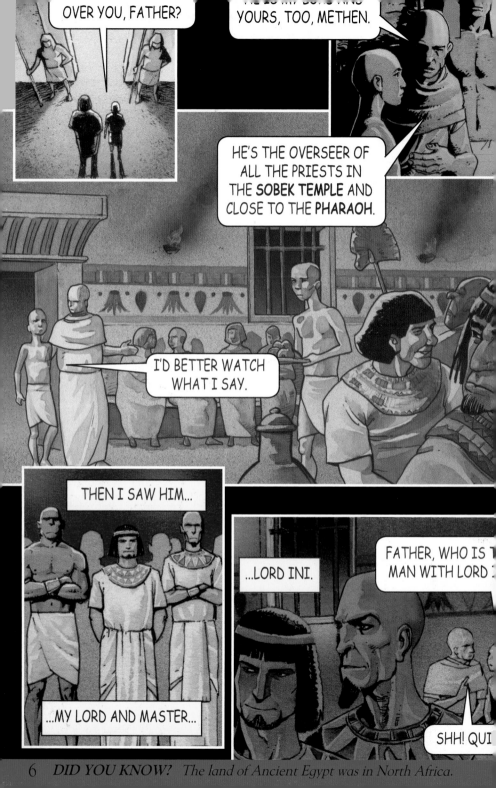

*DID YOU KNOW?*   The land of Ancient Egypt was in North Africa.

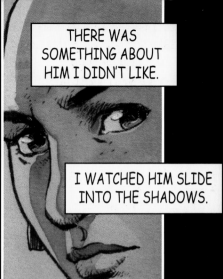

**_DID YOU KNOW?_** _Most Ancient Egyptian towns were surrounded by high_

*DID YOU KNOW?* The first Egyptian pyramid was built in 2650 BC

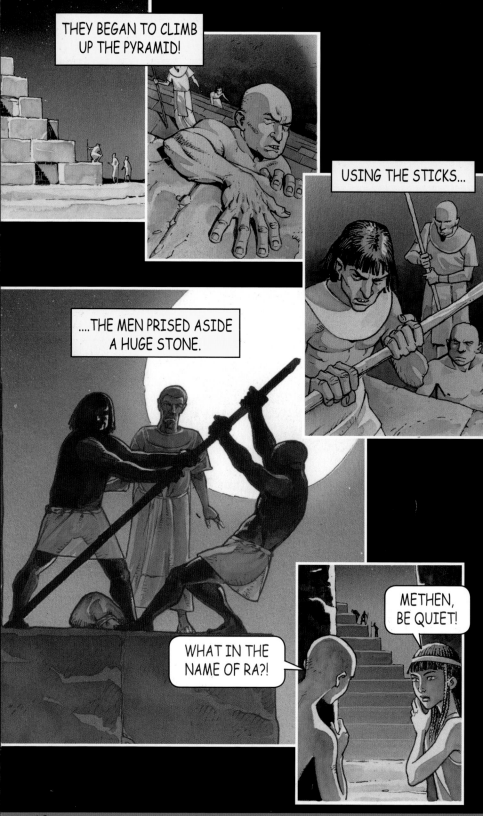

*DID YOU KNOW?* *Ra was the Sun god.*

TOMB ROBBERS!

THEY VANISHED INTO THE PYRAMID!

LET'S FOLLOW!

MADJA, LOO

IT WAS A SECRET PASSAGEWAY LEADING INTO THE PYRAMID.

THE PASSAGEWAY WAS HOT AND DARK. THE AIR WAS STALE.

*The Great Pyramid was made of more than 2 million stone blocks.*

*DID YOU KNOW?* Pyramids had trap doors to capture robbers.

WE SAW A LIGHT AHEAD.

IT'S THE **BURIAL CHAMBER!**

THESE JARS HAVE BEEN OPENED.

IT WAS CLEAR WHY KENAMUN HAD COME.

IT WAS THEN THAT I SAW THE **WRITING** ON THE WALL.

WHAT DOES IT SAY?

"CURSED BE HE WHO DESECRATES MY TOMB."

"MAY THE GREAT GOD SOBEK TEAR HIS LIMBS..."

"...AND CAST HIS SOUL INTO THE PIT OF EVERLASTING PAIN."

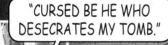

*A curse was a calling on a god to do someone harm.*

*DID YOU KNOW?* The burial chambers were full of treasure.

*DID YOU KNOW?* In Ancient Egypt, eyes were a symbol of protection.

Coffins had eyes painted on them so that the dead could "see".

THE NEXT DAY, NEWS SPREAD OF THE THEFT.

SOLDIERS WERE EVERYWHERE.

I WAS VERY FRIGHTENED.

TAKING A RISK, I WENT TO FIND KENAMUN...

...IN THE HOUSE OF THE DEAD.

WHEN I GOT THERE, THEY WERE BUSY MAKING **MUMMIES**.

JUST AS I STARTED TO LOOK AROUND...

DID YOU KNOW? *It took 70 days to make a mummy.*

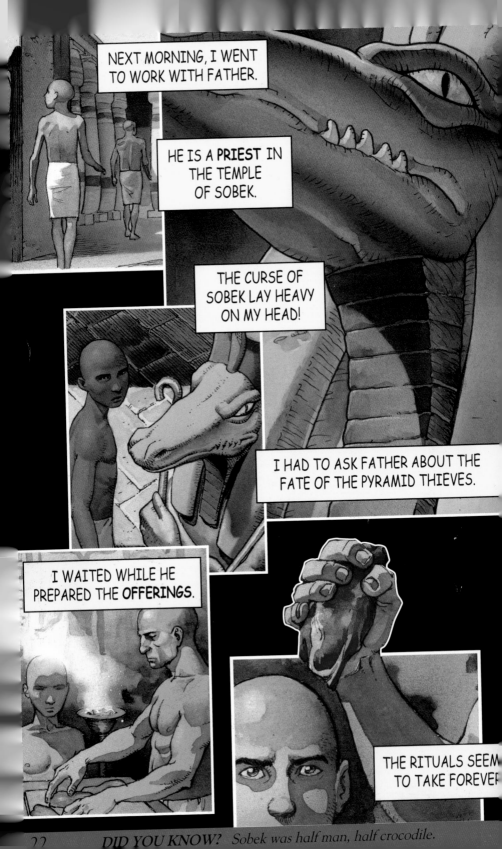

NEXT MORNING, I WENT TO WORK WITH FATHER.

HE IS A **PRIEST** IN THE TEMPLE OF SOBEK.

THE CURSE OF SOBEK LAY HEAVY ON MY HEAD!

I HAD TO ASK FATHER ABOUT THE FATE OF THE PYRAMID THIEVES.

I WAITED WHILE HE PREPARED THE **OFFERINGS**.

THE RITUALS SEEM TO TAKE FOREVER

*DID YOU KNOW?* Sobek was half man, half crocodile.

I ASKED FATHER.

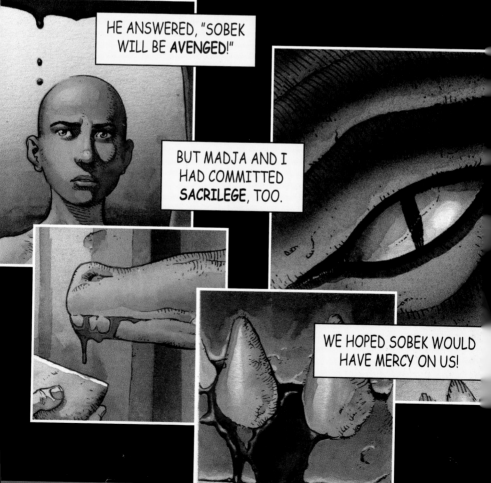

HE ANSWERED, "SOBEK WILL BE **AVENGED!**"

BUT MADJA AND I HAD COMMITTED **SACRILEGE**, TOO.

WE HOPED SOBEK WOULD HAVE MERCY ON US!

*Real crocodiles lived in the Temple of Sobek.*

I MET MADJA THAT EVENING BY **THE NILE**.

WE DECIDED TO SEARCH KENAMUN'S **BOAT**.

THERE IT IS!

LISTEN...SOMEON DOWN THERE.

TWO GUARDS WERE TALKING.

HAVE YOU HEARD ABOUT NAKHT AND OLD IAHAMES WITH THE LIMP?

NO, WHAT'S HAPPENED?

*DID YOU KNOW? Ancient Egypt grew up alongside the River Nile.*

...LORD INI SUSPECTS POISON!

THEY WERE FOUND IN THE DESERT...

...NO MARKS ON THEIR BODIES...

KENAMUN KNOWS ABOUT POISONS!

THE GUARDS LEFT.

RISKING ALL, WE MADE OUR WAY DOWN TO THE BOAT.

People in Ancient Egypt went almost everywhere by boat.

I STOOD GUARD AS MADJA STARTED TO SEARCH THE BOAT.

HURRY!

THERE WAS NO SIGN OF ANY STOLEN TREASURE.

I KNEW WE HAD TO BE QUICK...

THERE'S NOTHING HERE!

...I DIDN'T REALISE HOW QUICK!

**DID YOU KNOW?** *The River Nile flooded every year.*

The river was full of dangerous animals such as crocodiles and hippos.

*DID YOU KNOW?* Hippos weigh about 1,000 kg (2,500 pounds).

The Ancient Egyptians hunted hippos with spears.

*DID YOU KNOW?* Papyrus grows up to 3 metres (10 feet) tall.

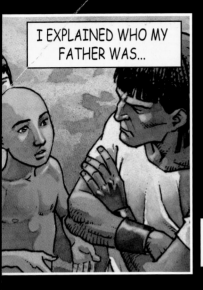

I EXPLAINED WHO MY FATHER WAS...

...AND WE WERE GRANTED AN AUDIENCE WITH HIS LORDSHIP.

WE WERE EXPLAINING OUR INCREDIBLE STORY WHEN...

...TRUMPETS BLARED AND THE DOORS WERE FLUNG OPEN.

IT WAS THE PHARAOH!

THE MIGHTY **SOBEKNEFERU**!

*DID YOU KNOW? Sobekneferu was a female pharaoh.*

She sometimes wore a fake beard to look like a male pharaoh.

33

*DID YOU KNOW?* The Ancient Egyptians called Egypt "Kemet".

*"Kemet" means "black land" – the soil left by the Nile flood water was black.* 35

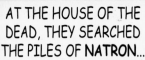
AT THE HOUSE OF THE DEAD, THEY SEARCHED THE PILES OF **NATRON**...

...UNRAVELLED BANDAGES...

...AND OPENED POTS

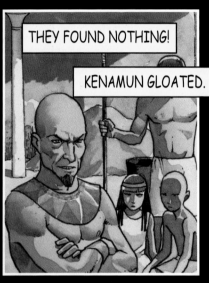
THEY FOUND NOTHING!

KENAMUN GLOATED.

TAKE THEM AWAY TO THE PLACE OF **EXECUTION**!

I HAD TO THINK OF SOMETHING!

THERE WAS ONE OTHER PLACE...

...IT HAD TO BE WORTH A TRY!

*DID YOU KNOW?* Natron was used for drying out bodie

I HANDED THE **PRECIOUS OBJECT** TO LORD INI.

THIS AMULET WAS MADE FOR THE LAST PHARAOH.

I CAN EXPLAIN...

THE SOLDIERS TURNED TO KENAMUN.

SUDDENLY, HE PUSHED LORD INI AWAY...

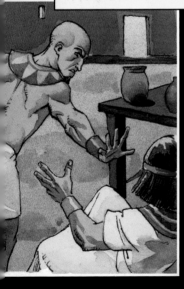

...KNOCKED OVER A TABLE OF NATRON POTS...

*DID YOU KNOW?* An amulet was meant to bring good luck.

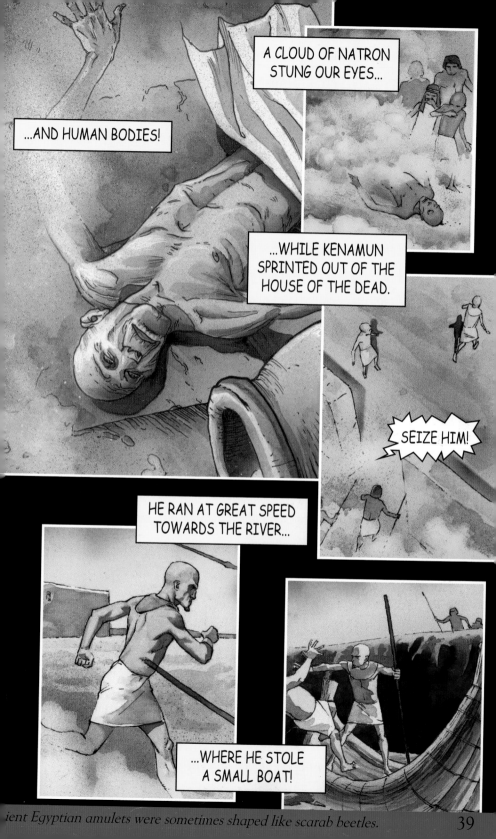

**DID YOU KNOW?** *Small reed boats were pushed along with poles.*

KENAMUN SWAM FOR HIS LIFE...

...BUT HE COULDN'T OUTSWIM THE GODS.

THE CURSE OF LORD SOBEK HAD COME TRUE!

HE'S GONE TO FACE THE JUSTICE OF **OSIRIS**!

THE END

*Nile crocodiles have up to 68 sharp teeth.*

| King Menes unites Egypt | Pharaoh Sobekneferu comes to the throne | Death of Pharaoh Rameses III |
|---|---|---|
| 3100 | c. 1799 | 1153 |

3000 BCE (BEFORE COMMON ERA)  2000 BCE  YOU ARE HERE  1000 BCE

## ANCIENT EGYPT

Ancient Egypt flourished in North Africa from about 4000 BCE to 332 CE. It grew up on a strip of fertile land, never more than a few kilometres wide, that lay on either side of the River Nile. Fed by rains falling to the south, the Nile snakes through the African desert until it reaches the Mediterranean Sea.

Great Pyramid at Giza · Memphis · Hawara · EGYPT · RIVER NILE · Thebes · Valley of the Kings

# GLOSSARY

## TOWN                          PAGE 5

Most towns in Ancient Egypt were crowded with many houses, crammed together in unplanned streets. The houses were made of mud bricks baked in the sun.

## PHARAOH                    PAGE 6

At the top of Egyptian society was the king called a pharaoh. He was considered a god by the Egyptians and above the normal rules of society. Most pharaohs were men, but a few women ruled Ancient Egypt at different times.

Female pharaoh Hatshepsut

## SOBEK TEMPLE              PAGE 6

Sobek was the crocodile god. He was praised all over Egypt in temples, where priests guarded, cared for and worshipped the god's image day and night. The priests even prepared meals for the god.

Picture of Sobek on the temple wall

| Roman Empire collapsing | | Columbus sails to America | | US astronauts land on the Moon |
| --- | --- | --- | --- | --- |
| | 410 | | 1492 | 1969 |

TIMELINE

1 CE (COMMON ERA)          1000 CE          2000 CE

## MARRIAGE          PAGE 9

Most marriages in Ancient Egypt were arranged by the girl's father and mother. Girls would marry at around 13 years of age and boys at 16. A scribe could draw up a contract giving equal rights to husband and wife.

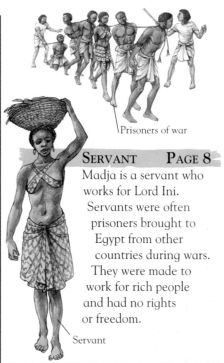

Prisoners of war

## SERVANT          PAGE 8

Madja is a servant who works for Lord Ini. Servants were often prisoners brought to Egypt from other countries during wars. They were made to work for rich people and had no rights or freedom.

Servant

Groom

Bride

Scribe

## CHIEF EMBALMER          PAGE 7

The Chief Embalmer was in charge of mummifying bodies to preserve them. The Ancient Egyptians believed this helped people live forever. The Chief Embalmer wore a jackal's mask that symbolised Anubis, the god of the dead.

Chief Embalmer

## LORD INI'S PALACE          PAGE 9

Lord Ini was a rich nobleman who lived in a large palace. The house was expensively decorated, and the interior walls were brightly painted with pictures of people, ducks and lotus flowers (a type of lily).

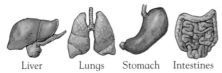
Liver    Lungs    Stomach    Intestines

## ENTRAILS        PAGE 9

The entrails are the internal organs of
a dead person, such as the intestines.
These were removed when a body was
mummified and stored in special jars.

The Great Pyramid

The burial chamber

## PYRAMID        PAGE 11

The pyramids were burial tombs for
the pharaohs and their queens. The
biggest one ever built was the Great
Pyramid built during the reign of
Pharaoh Khufu (2589–2566 BCE).

## TOMB ROBBERS        PAGE 13

The pyramids were full of valuable
things that the pharaoh might need in
the afterlife. Although the tombs had
secret passages and rooms, they were
easy for robbers to dig their way into.

## BURIAL CHAMBER        PAGE 15

The body of the pharaoh was buried in
the burial chamber hidden deep inside
the pyramid. Its whereabouts were
meant to be a secret, but since many
helped build the temple, the room was
often easy for robbers to find.

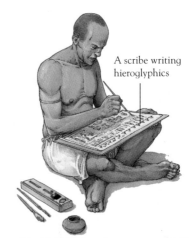

A scribe writing
hieroglyphics

## WRITING        PAGE 15

Ancient Egyptian writing was a type
of picture writing called hieroglyphics.
Only scribes like Methen could read
and write.

## COFFIN    PAGE 17

The mummy was placed
in a wooden coffin case
that was often shaped
like a person. The coffin
was often painted with
pictures and hieroglyphics.

Mummy
wrapped in
bandages

## MUMMIES    PAGE 20

The embalmed bodies of
the dead were called
mummies. After they were
dried out and the organs
removed, the bodies were
usually wrapped in bandages.

Coffin case

## SOLDIERS    PAGE 20

Soldiers were workers forced to serve
the pharaoh. They carried spears and
shields but wore little armour.

## SCROLL    PAGE 21

Scribes wrote on sheets of papyrus
paper that were rolled up into scrolls.
Papyrus was a plant that grew beside
the River Nile.

## HOUSE OF THE DEAD    PAGE 20

Dead bodies were mummified in the
House of the Dead in a ritual that
lasted 70 days. They were dried so
that they did not
rot and then
usually wrapped
in bandages.

Soldier

General

## PRIEST    PAGE 22

Priests like Methen's father performed important religious ceremonies, or rituals. They were important people in Egyptian life.

Priest

## OFFERINGS    PAGE 22

The priests prepared food and other offerings for the gods. Sobek, the crocodile god, was offered honey cakes and meat.

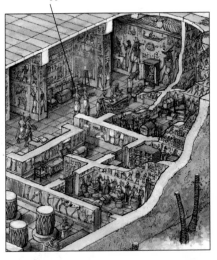

Only the priests could approach the shrine of Sobek

## AVENGED    PAGE 23

Methen's father believes the god Sobek will harm the pyramid thieves in return for their wrongdoing, which means Sobek will be avenged.

## SACRILEGE    PAGE 23

Offending a god is called sacrilege. Methen and Madja believe they offended the god Sobek by entering the pyramid and breaking a coffin. They believe they were cursed by him.

## BOAT    PAGE 24

Nile boats were made of bundles of papyrus reeds. Cargo boats transported heavy goods such as building stone.

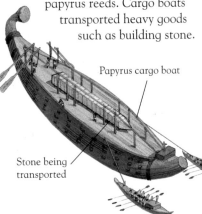

Papyrus cargo boat

Stone being transported

## THE NILE    PAGE 24

The civilisation of Ancient Egypt depended on the River Nile. Every year, the river flooded the surrounding countryside, making the land better for growing crops when the water receded.

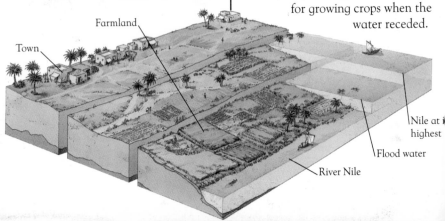

Farmland

Town

Nile at highest

Flood water

River Nile

46

## Betrothed      Page 27

Madja is betrothed to Kenamun, which means she is going to marry him.

## Hippos      Page 29

The Nile waters were home to hippos, who were a danger to boats.

A hippo hunt

## Papyrus reeds      Page 30

Papyrus reeds grew on the banks of the Nile. They were used for many things including boats, baskets, ropes and paper.

## Sobekneferu      Page 32

The mighty Sobekneferu was a female pharaoh who reigned for about four years. Her name means "Beauties of Sobek".

The pharaoh

Scribe

People paying their respects to the pharaoh

47

Natron powder being poured on a dead body

## PRECIOUS OBJECT    PAGE 38

Precious objects, such as the amulet Methen found, were valuable items. They were put in the tomb in case the pharaoh needed them in the afterlife.

This necklace is a precious object

## NATRON    PAGE 36

Natron was a salt-like substance used to dry out dead bodies when they were being made into mummies. The white powder was mined from dry lake beds near the River Nile.

## EXECUTION    PAGE 36

The most common punishment in Egypt was beating, but serious crimes could be punished by execution, which means being put to death.

Prisoners being beaten

## HORUS    PAGE 40

Horus was an Egyptian god with a hawk's head. The Horus-eye was a symbol of healing and protection.

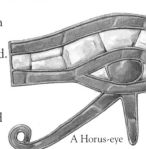
A Horus-eye

## OSIRIS    PAGE 41

Osiris was the god of death and rebirth. He judged the dead in the Underworld. Only those who had led good lives were granted eternal life.

Osiris and his wife Isis

Horus